P9-BYY-900

Bugs in the Garden

by Catherine Hapka
illustrated by Mike Byrne

Scholastic Inc.

ISBN 978-0-545-82339-5

Text copyright © 2015 by Catherine Hapka
Illustrations copyright © 2015 by Mike Byrne

Published by Scholastic Inc. SCHOLASTIC and associated logos are trademarks and/or registered trademarks of Scholastic Inc.

10 9 8 7 6 5 4 3 2 1   15 16 17 18 19/0

Printed in the U.S.A.   40

First printing, March 2015

Emma is in kindergarten.

Emma loves school.
She loves to learn.

"I hope we do something fun today," she tells Abby, Ben, and Jack.

Ms. Green comes in.
"It is spring," she says.
"Let's have class in the garden."

"Hooray!" Jack cheers.

"Get your notebooks and crayons,"
Ms. Green says.
"Then follow me."

Ms. Green leads the class outside.
Everyone is happy.
What will they learn in the garden?

"Look around," Ms. Green says.
"What do you see?"

"I see flowers," Abby says.
"I see trees," Emma says.
"I see cool bugs!" Jack says.

"That is right, Jack," Ms. Green says.
"Today we will learn about bugs."

"Look for bugs in the garden,"
says Ms. Green.
"Then draw the ones you find."

14

"I will find a lot of bugs!"
Roberto says.
"Me, too!" Gavin says.

"Draw as many bugs as you can,"
Ms. Green says.

Emma looks around.
A fly buzzes past.
A cricket hops by.
What should she draw first?

Then Emma sees a butterfly.
It lands on a flower.

Emma

"So pretty," Emma says.
"I will draw you first!"

Drawing the butterfly is hard!
Its wings have lots of spots.
Emma wants to get them just right.
She goes close to the butterfly.

The butterfly flies away.
"Wait!" Emma says.
She follows it.

The butterfly lands on another flower.

"Good!" Emma says.

"Stay there, please."

Emma follows the butterfly
around the garden.
It flies here and there.
Emma works on her picture.

Then Ben and Jack run over.
They scare the butterfly away.
But it's okay.
Emma's picture is all done.

"How many bugs did you draw?"
Emma asks.
"Five!" Jack says.
"Four," Ben says.

"I only drew one," Emma says.

She is worried.

Will there be time to find more?

Ms. Green claps her hands.
"Time to go back inside!" she calls.

Jack

The class walks back inside.
The kids show their pictures.
Everyone drew four or five
bugs.
Abby drew six!

"I only drew one bug," Emma tells
Jack and Ben.
She is sad.

Then it is Emma's turn.
"Look at that cool bug!"
Ms. Green says.
"Good job, Emma."

"Really?" Emma says.

"Yes, it is perfect," Ms. Green says.

"Let's begin our lesson on butterflies."

Hooray!
Emma cannot wait to go
back to the garden!